Angel Journal

Daily
Guidance

Angel Journal Daily Guidance: A Spiritual Journal for Writing about Messages and Signs from your Angels

Published by Angel Journal and Books
Burlington, ON, Canada. 2018

First Edition: First Publication

ISBN-13: 978-1-9994486-3-9

This Angel Journal Belongs To

_____

Contact Information

marysusanmclellan@gmail.com

Angeljournal.com

Innerselfhealing.com

Other Journals and Books

Angel Journal 3 Card Spreads (color edition)

Angel Journal 3 Card Spreads (grayscale edition)

Walking in God's Garden: A Gratitude Prayer Journal

I Intend to be More not Less: An Intention Planner, Calendar, and Journal

Sacral Chakra Tune Up for Women: Use the Power of Journaling,

The Joy of Coloring to Raise your Vibes and Claim your Power

Restore Yourself with Inner Truth: A Coloring Book Journal

Kindly Leave a Review on Amazon and Support the Use of Journaling

For health, well-being, peace, and empowerment.

A Prayer of Invocation

Dear God, Creator of all that is,

Divine Mother and Arch Angel Michael,

I ask that you surround and protect me

And clear my space so that I may receive your guidance.

I ask that I be given guidance that

I can understand so that

I may take guided action today.

I ask that the messages that

I receive today be

In alignment with my Highest Good

And for the purpose of my well-being.

Thankyou Creator and so it is.

Date: _____ Situation: _____

Question _____

_____

Card or Sign: _____

_____

Keywords: _____

_____

Images of note: _____

_____

First Reaction to Sign, Event or Card

My Intuitive Response

Angel Guidance

Notes

Angel Journal

Date: _____ Situation: _____

Question _____

_____

Card or Sign: _____

_____

Keywords: _____

_____

Images of note: _____

_____

First Reaction to Sign, Event or Card

My Intuitive Response

Angel Guidance

Notes

Angel Journal

Date: _____ Situation: _____

Question _____
_____

Card or Sign: _____
_____

Keywords: _____
_____

Images of note: _____
_____

First Reaction to Sign, Event or Card

My Intuitive Response

Angel Guidance

Notes

Angel Journal

Date: _____ Situation: _____

Question _____

_____

Card or Sign: _____

_____

Keywords: _____

_____

Images of note: _____

_____

┌─────── First Reaction to Sign, Event or Card ───────┐

└──┘

┌─────────────── My Intuitive Response ───────────────┐

└──┘

┌───────────────── Angel Guidance ─────────────────┐

└──┘

┌───────────────────── Notes ─────────────────────┐

└──┘

Angel Journal

_____

_____

_____

_____

_____

_____

_____

_____

_____

_____

_____

_____

_____

_____

_____

_____

Date: _____ Situation: _____

Question _____

_____

Card or Sign: _____

_____

Keywords: _____

_____

Images of note: _____

_____

First Reaction to Sign, Event or Card

My Intuitive Response

Angel Guidance

Notes

Angel Journal

Date: _____ Situation: _____

Question _____

_____

Card or Sign: _____

_____

Keywords: _____

_____

Images of note: _____

_____

First Reaction to Sign, Event or Card

My Intuitive Response

Angel Guidance

Notes

Angel Journal

Date: _____ Situation: _____

Question _____

_____

Card or Sign: _____

_____

Keywords: _____

_____

Images of note: _____

_____

First Reaction to Sign, Event or Card

My Intuitive Response

Angel Guidance

Notes

Angel Journal

Date: _____ Situation: _____

Question _____

_____

Card or Sign: _____

_____

Keywords: _____

_____

Images of note: _____

_____

First Reaction to Sign, Event or Card

My Intuitive Response

Angel Guidance

Notes

Angel Journal

Date: _____ Situation: _____

Question _____

_____

Card or Sign: _____

Keywords: _____

Images of note: _____

_____

First Reaction to Sign, Event or Card

My Intuitive Response

Angel Guidance

Notes

Angel Journal

Date: _____ Situation: _____

Question _____

_____

Card or Sign: _____

_____

Keywords: _____

_____

Images of note: _____

_____

First Reaction to Sign, Event or Card

My Intuitive Response

Angel Guidance

Notes

Angel Journal

Date: _____ Situation: _____

Question _____

_____

Card or Sign: _____

_____

Keywords: _____

_____

Images of note: _____

_____

First Reaction to Sign, Event or Card

My Intuitive Response

Angel Guidance

Notes

Angel Journal

Date: _____ Situation: _____

Question _____

_____

Card or Sign: _____

_____

Keywords: _____

_____

Images of note: _____

_____

First Reaction to Sign, Event or Card

My Intuitive Response

Angel Guidance

Notes

Angel Journal

Date: _____ Situation: _____

Question _____

_____

Card or Sign: _____

_____

Keywords: _____

_____

Images of note: _____

_____

```
┌─────────── First Reaction to Sign, Event or Card ───────────┐
│                                                             │
│                                                             │
│                                                             │
│                                                             │
└─────────────────────────────────────────────────────────────┘
```

```
┌─────────────── My Intuitive Response ───────────────┐
│                                                      │
│                                                      │
│                                                      │
└──────────────────────────────────────────────────────┘
```

```
┌─────────────────── Angel Guidance ───────────────────┐
│                                                       │
│                                                       │
│                                                       │
└───────────────────────────────────────────────────────┘
```

```
┌─────────────────────── Notes ───────────────────────┐
│                                                      │
│                                                      │
│                                                      │
│                                                      │
└──────────────────────────────────────────────────────┘
```

Angel Journal

Date: _____ Situation: _____

Question _____

_____

Card or Sign: _____

_____

Keywords: _____

_____

Images of note: _____

_____

```
First Reaction to Sign, Event or Card
```

```
My Intuitive Response
```

```
Angel Guidance
```

```
Notes
```

Angel Journal

Date: _____ Situation: _____

Question _____

_____

Card or Sign: _____

_____

Keywords: _____

_____

Images of note: _____

_____

┌─────────────── First Reaction to Sign, Event or Card ───────────────┐
│   │
│   │
│   │
│   │
└──┘

┌─────────────────────── My Intuitive Response ───────────────────────┐
│   │
│   │
│   │
│   │
└──┘

┌────────────────────────── Angel Guidance ──────────────────────────┐
│   │
│   │
│   │
└──┘

┌───────────────────────────── Notes ─────────────────────────────────┐
│   │
│   │
│   │
│   │
└──┘

Angel Journal

Date: _____ Situation: _____

Question _____

_____

Card or Sign: _____

_____

Keywords: _____

_____

Images of note: _____

_____

First Reaction to Sign, Event or Card

My Intuitive Response

Angel Guidance

Notes

Angel Journal

Date: _____ Situation: _____

Question _____

_____

Card or Sign: _____

_____

Keywords: _____

_____

Images of note: _____

_____

First Reaction to Sign, Event or Card

My Intuitive Response

Angel Guidance

Notes

Angel Journal

Date: _____ Situation: _____

Question _____

_____

Card or Sign: _____

_____

Keywords: _____

_____

Images of note: _____

_____

First Reaction to Sign, Event or Card

My Intuitive Response

Angel Guidance

Notes

Angel Journal

Date: _____ Situation: _____

Question _____

_____

Card or Sign: _____

_____

Keywords: _____

_____

Images of note: _____

_____

First Reaction to Sign, Event or Card

My Intuitive Response

Angel Guidance

Notes

Angel Journal

Date: _____ Situation: _____

Question _____

_____

Card or Sign: _____

_____

Keywords: _____

_____

Images of note: _____

_____

First Reaction to Sign, Event or Card

My Intuitive Response

Angel Guidance

Notes

Angel Journal

Date: _____ Situation: _____

Question _____

_____

Card or Sign: _____

_____

Keywords: _____

_____

Images of note: _____

_____

First Reaction to Sign, Event or Card

My Intuitive Response

Angel Guidance

Notes

Angel Journal

Date: _____ Situation: _____

Question _____

_____

Card or Sign: _____

_____

Keywords: _____

_____

Images of note: _____

_____

First Reaction to Sign, Event or Card

My Intuitive Response

Angel Guidance

Notes

Angel Journal

Date: _____ Situation: _____

Question _____

_____

Card or Sign: _____

_____

Keywords: _____

_____

Images of note: _____

_____

First Reaction to Sign, Event or Card

My Intuitive Response

Angel Guidance

Notes

Angel Journal

Date: _____ Situation: _____

Question _____

_____

Card or Sign: _____

_____

Keywords: _____

_____

Images of note: _____

_____

First Reaction to Sign, Event or Card

My Intuitive Response

Angel Guidance

Notes

Angel Journal

Date: _____ Situation: _____

Question _____

_____

Card or Sign: _____

Keywords: _____

Images of note: _____

First Reaction to Sign, Event or Card

My Intuitive Response

Angel Guidance

Notes

Angel Journal

_____

_____

_____

_____

_____

_____

_____

_____

_____

_____

_____

_____

_____

_____

_____

Date: _____ Situation: _____

Question _____

_____

Card or Sign: _____

_____

Keywords: _____

_____

Images of note: _____

_____

First Reaction to Sign, Event or Card

My Intuitive Response

Angel Guidance

Notes

Angel Journal

Date: _____ Situation: _____

Question _____

_____

Card or Sign: _____

_____

Keywords: _____

_____

Images of note: _____

_____

┌─────────── First Reaction to Sign, Event or Card ───────────┐
│   │
│   │
│   │
│   │
└──┘

┌────────────────── My Intuitive Response ──────────────────┐
│   │
│   │
│   │
└──┘

┌──────────────────── Angel Guidance ────────────────────┐
│   │
│   │
│   │
└───┘

┌─────────────────────── Notes ───────────────────────┐
│   │
│   │
│   │
│   │
└──┘

Angel Journal

Date: _____ Situation: _____

Question _____

_____

Card or Sign: _____

Keywords: _____

Images of note: _____

```
┌─────────── First Reaction to Sign, Event or Card ───────────┐
│                                                             │
│                                                             │
│                                                             │
│                                                             │
└─────────────────────────────────────────────────────────────┘

┌─────────────────── My Intuitive Response ───────────────────┐
│                                                             │
│                                                             │
│                                                             │
└─────────────────────────────────────────────────────────────┘

┌────────────────────── Angel Guidance ───────────────────────┐
│                                                             │
│                                                             │
│                                                             │
└─────────────────────────────────────────────────────────────┘

┌─────────────────────────── Notes ───────────────────────────┐
│                                                             │
│                                                             │
│                                                             │
│                                                             │
└─────────────────────────────────────────────────────────────┘
```

Angel Journal

_____

_____

_____

_____

_____

_____

_____

_____

_____

_____

_____

_____

_____

_____

_____

Date: _____ Situation: _____

Question _____

_____

Card or Sign: _____

_____

Keywords: _____

_____

Images of note: _____

_____

| First Reaction to Sign, Event or Card |
| |
| |
| |
| |

| My Intuitive Response |
| |
| |
| |

| Angel Guidance |
| |
| |
| |

| Notes |
| |
| |
| |
| |

Angel Journal

Date: _____ Situation: _____

Question _____

_____

Card or Sign: _____

_____

Keywords: _____

_____

Images of note: _____

_____

First Reaction to Sign, Event or Card

My Intuitive Response

Angel Guidance

Notes

Angel Journal

Date: _____ Situation: _____

Question _____

_____

Card or Sign: _____

_____

Keywords: _____

_____

Images of note: _____

_____

First Reaction to Sign, Event or Card

My Intuitive Response

Angel Guidance

Notes

Angel Journal

Date: _____ Situation: _____

Question _____

_____

Card or Sign: _____

_____

Keywords: _____

_____

Images of note: _____

_____

First Reaction to Sign, Event or Card

My Intuitive Response

Angel Guidance

Notes

Angel Journal

Date: _____ Situation: _____

Question _____

_____

Card or Sign: _____

_____

Keywords: _____

_____

Images of note: _____

_____

First Reaction to Sign, Event or Card

My Intuitive Response

Angel Guidance

Notes

Angel Journal

_____

_____

_____

_____

_____

_____

_____

_____

_____

_____

_____

_____

_____

_____

_____

Date: _____ Situation: _____

Question _____

_____

Card or Sign: _____

_____

Keywords: _____

_____

Images of note: _____

_____

First Reaction to Sign, Event or Card

My Intuitive Response

Angel Guidance

Notes

Angel Journal

Date: _____ Situation: _____

Question _____

_____

Card or Sign: _____

_____

Keywords: _____

_____

Images of note: _____

_____

First Reaction to Sign, Event or Card

My Intuitive Response

Angel Guidance

Notes

Angel Journal

Date: _____ Situation: _____

Question _____

_____

Card or Sign: _____

_____

Keywords: _____

_____

Images of note: _____

_____

┌─── First Reaction to Sign, Event or Card ───┐

└───┘

┌─────────── My Intuitive Response ───────────┐

└───┘

┌─────────────── Angel Guidance ───────────────┐

└───┘

┌──────────────────── Notes ────────────────────┐

└───┘

Angel Journal

Date: _____ Situation: _____

Question _____

_____

Card or Sign: _____

Keywords: _____

Images of note: _____

First Reaction to Sign, Event or Card

My Intuitive Response

Angel Guidance

Notes

Angel Journal

Date: _____ Situation: _____

Question _____

_____

Card or Sign: _____

Keywords: _____

Images of note: _____

First Reaction to Sign, Event or Card

My Intuitive Response

Angel Guidance

Notes

Angel Journal

Date: _____ Situation: _____

Question _____

_____

Card or Sign: _____

_____

Keywords: _____

_____

Images of note: _____

_____

First Reaction to Sign, Event or Card

My Intuitive Response

Angel Guidance

Notes

Angel Journal

Date: _____ Situation: _____

Question _____

_____

Card or Sign: _____

_____

Keywords: _____

_____

Images of note: _____

_____

First Reaction to Sign, Event or Card

My Intuitive Response

Angel Guidance

Notes

Angel Journal

_____

_____

_____

_____

_____

_____

_____

_____

_____

_____

_____

_____

_____

_____

_____

_____

Date: _____ Situation: _____

Question _____

_____

Card or Sign: _____

_____

Keywords: _____

_____

Images of note: _____

_____

First Reaction to Sign, Event or Card

My Intuitive Response

Angel Guidance

Notes

Angel Journal

Date: _____ Situation: _____

Question _____

_____

Card or Sign: _____

_____

Keywords: _____

_____

Images of note: _____

_____

First Reaction to Sign, Event or Card

My Intuitive Response

Angel Guidance

Notes

Angel Journal

_____

_____

_____

_____

_____

_____

_____

_____

_____

_____

_____

_____

_____

_____

_____

Date: _____ Situation: _____

Question _____

_____

Card or Sign: _____

_____

Keywords: _____

_____

Images of note: _____

_____

First Reaction to Sign, Event or Card

My Intuitive Response

Angel Guidance

Notes

Angel Journal

Date: _____ Situation: _____

Question _____

_____

Card or Sign: _____

_____

Keywords: _____

_____

Images of note: _____

_____

| First Reaction to Sign, Event or Card |

| My Intuitive Response |

| Angel Guidance |

| Notes |

Angel Journal

Date: _____ Situation: _____

Question _____

_____

Card or Sign: _____

_____

Keywords: _____

_____

Images of note: _____

_____

First Reaction to Sign, Event or Card

My Intuitive Response

Angel Guidance

Notes

Angel Journal

Date: _____ Situation: _____

Question _____

_____

Card or Sign: _____

_____

Keywords: _____

_____

Images of note: _____

_____

First Reaction to Sign, Event or Card

My Intuitive Response

Angel Guidance

Notes

Angel Journal

Date: _____ Situation: _____

Question _____

_____

Card or Sign: _____

_____

Keywords: _____

_____

Images of note: _____

_____

First Reaction to Sign, Event or Card

My Intuitive Response

Angel Guidance

Notes

Angel Journal

Date: _____ Situation: _____

Question _____

_____

Card or Sign: _____

_____

Keywords: _____

_____

Images of note: _____

_____

┌─────────── First Reaction to Sign, Event or Card ───────────┐
│   │
│   │
│   │
│   │
└───┘

┌──────────────── My Intuitive Response ────────────────┐
│   │
│   │
│   │
└──┘

┌──────────────── Angel Guidance ────────────────┐
│   │
│   │
│   │
└───┘

┌──────────────── Notes ────────────────┐
│   │
│   │
│   │
│   │
└──┘

Angel Journal

Date: _____ Situation: _____

Question _____

_____

Card or Sign: _____

_____

Keywords: _____

_____

Images of note: _____

_____

First Reaction to Sign, Event or Card

My Intuitive Response

Angel Guidance

Notes

Angel Journal

Date: _____ Situation: _____

Question _____

_____

Card or Sign: _____

_____

Keywords: _____

_____

Images of note: _____

_____

First Reaction to Sign, Event or Card

My Intuitive Response

Angel Guidance

Notes

Angel Journal

Date: _____ Situation: _____

Question _____

_____

Card or Sign: _____

_____

Keywords: _____

_____

Images of note: _____

_____

First Reaction to Sign, Event or Card

My Intuitive Response

Angel Guidance

Notes

Angel Journal

Date: _____ Situation: _____

Question _____
_____

Card or Sign: _____

Keywords: _____

Images of note: _____

First Reaction to Sign, Event or Card

My Intuitive Response

Angel Guidance

Notes

Angel Journal

Date: _____ Situation: _____

Question _____

_____

Card or Sign: _____

_____

Keywords: _____

_____

Images of note: _____

_____

First Reaction to Sign, Event or Card

My Intuitive Response

Angel Guidance

Notes

Angel Journal

Date: _____ Situation: _____

Question _____

_____

Card or Sign: _____

_____

Keywords: _____

_____

Images of note: _____

_____

First Reaction to Sign, Event or Card

My Intuitive Response

Angel Guidance

Notes

Angel Journal

Date: _____ Situation: _____

Question _____

_____

Card or Sign: _____

Keywords: _____

Images of note: _____

First Reaction to Sign, Event or Card

My Intuitive Response

Angel Guidance

Notes

Angel Journal

Date: _____ Situation: _____

Question _____

_____

Card or Sign: _____

_____

Keywords: _____

_____

Images of note: _____

_____

| First Reaction to Sign, Event or Card |

| My Intuitive Response |

| Angel Guidance |

| Notes |

Angel Journal

Date: _____ Situation: _____

Question _____

_____

Card or Sign: _____

_____

Keywords: _____

_____

Images of note: _____

_____

| First Reaction to Sign, Event or Card |

| My Intuitive Response |

| Angel Guidance |

| Notes |

Angel Journal

Date: _____ Situation: _____

Question _____

_____

Card or Sign: _____

_____

Keywords: _____

_____

Images of note: _____

_____

First Reaction to Sign, Event or Card

My Intuitive Response

Angel Guidance

Notes

Angel Journal

Date: _____ Situation: _____

Question _____

_____

Card or Sign: _____

_____

Keywords: _____

_____

Images of note: _____

_____

First Reaction to Sign, Event or Card

My Intuitive Response

Angel Guidance

Notes

Angel Journal

_____

_____

_____

_____

_____

_____

_____

_____

_____

_____

_____

_____

_____

_____

_____

_____

Date: _____ Situation: _____

Question _____

_____

Card or Sign: _____

_____

Keywords: _____

_____

Images of note: _____

_____

First Reaction to Sign, Event or Card

My Intuitive Response

Angel Guidance

Notes

Angel Journal

Date: _____ Situation: _____

Question _____

_____

Card or Sign: _____

_____

Keywords: _____

_____

Images of note: _____

_____

First Reaction to Sign, Event or Card

My Intuitive Response

Angel Guidance

Notes

Angel Journal

Date: _____ Situation: _____

Question _____

_____

Card or Sign: _____

_____

Keywords: _____

_____

Images of note: _____

_____

First Reaction to Sign, Event or Card

My Intuitive Response

Angel Guidance

Notes

Angel Journal

Date: _____ Situation: _____

Question _____

_____

Card or Sign: _____

_____

Keywords: _____

_____

Images of note: _____

First Reaction to Sign, Event or Card

My Intuitive Response

Angel Guidance

Notes

Angel Journal

Date: _____ Situation: _____

Question _____

_____

Card or Sign: _____

_____

Keywords: _____

_____

Images of note: _____

_____

First Reaction to Sign, Event or Card

My Intuitive Response

Angel Guidance

Notes

Angel Journal

Date: _____ Situation: _____

Question _____

_____

Card or Sign: _____

_____

Keywords: _____

_____

Images of note: _____

_____

First Reaction to Sign, Event or Card

My Intuitive Response

Angel Guidance

Notes

Angel Journal

_____

_____

_____

_____

_____

_____

_____

_____

_____

_____

_____

_____

_____

_____

_____

_____

Date: _____ Situation: _____

Question _____
_____

Card or Sign: _____
_____

Keywords: _____
_____

Images of note: _____
_____

First Reaction to Sign, Event or Card

My Intuitive Response

Angel Guidance

Notes

Angel Journal

_____

_____

_____

_____

_____

_____

_____

_____

_____

_____

_____

_____

_____

_____

_____

_____

Date: _____ Situation: _____

Question _____

_____

Card or Sign: _____

_____

Keywords: _____

_____

Images of note: _____

_____

First Reaction to Sign, Event or Card

My Intuitive Response

Angel Guidance

Notes

Angel Journal

Date: _____ Situation: _____

Question _____

_____

Card or Sign: _____

_____

Keywords: _____

_____

Images of note: _____

_____

First Reaction to Sign, Event or Card

My Intuitive Response

Angel Guidance

Notes

Angel Journal

Date: _____ Situation: _____

Question _____
_____

Card or Sign: _____
_____

Keywords: _____

Images of note: _____

First Reaction to Sign, Event or Card

My Intuitive Response

Angel Guidance

Notes

Angel Journal

Date: _____ Situation: _____

Question _____

_____

Card or Sign: _____

_____

Keywords: _____

_____

Images of note: _____

_____

First Reaction to Sign, Event or Card

My Intuitive Response

Angel Guidance

Notes

Angel Journal

Date: _____ Situation: _____

Question _____

_____

Card or Sign: _____

_____

Keywords: _____

_____

Images of note: _____

_____

First Reaction to Sign, Event or Card

My Intuitive Response

Angel Guidance

Notes

Angel Journal

_____

_____

_____

_____

_____

_____

_____

_____

_____

_____

_____

_____

_____

_____

_____

Date: _____ Situation: _____

Question _____

_____

Card or Sign: _____

_____

Keywords: _____

_____

Images of note: _____

_____

First Reaction to Sign, Event or Card

My Intuitive Response

Angel Guidance

Notes

Angel Journal

Date: _____ Situation: _____

Question _____

_____

Card or Sign: _____

_____

Keywords: _____

_____

Images of note: _____

_____

First Reaction to Sign, Event or Card

My Intuitive Response

Angel Guidance

Notes

Angel Journal

_____

_____

_____

_____

_____

_____

_____

_____

_____

_____

_____

_____

_____

_____

_____

_____

Date: _____ Situation: _____

Question _____

_____

Card or Sign: _____

Keywords: _____

Images of note: _____

First Reaction to Sign, Event or Card

My Intuitive Response

Angel Guidance

Notes

Angel Journal

Date: _____ Situation: _____

Question _____

_____

Card or Sign: _____

_____

Keywords: _____

_____

Images of note: _____

_____

First Reaction to Sign, Event or Card

My Intuitive Response

Angel Guidance

Notes

Angel Journal

Date: _____ Situation: _____

Question _____

_____

Card or Sign: _____

_____

Keywords: _____

_____

Images of note: _____

_____

First Reaction to Sign, Event or Card

My Intuitive Response

Angel Guidance

Notes

Angel Journal

Date: _____ Situation: _____

Question _____

_____

Card or Sign: _____

_____

Keywords: _____

_____

Images of note: _____

_____

First Reaction to Sign, Event or Card

My Intuitive Response

Angel Guidance

Notes

Angel Journal

Date: _____ Situation: _____

Question _____

_____

Card or Sign: _____

_____

Keywords: _____

_____

Images of note: _____

_____

First Reaction to Sign, Event or Card

My Intuitive Response

Angel Guidance

Notes

Angel Journal

_____

_____

_____

_____

_____

_____

_____

_____

_____

_____

_____

_____

_____

_____

_____

Date: _____ Situation: _____

Question _____

_____

Card or Sign: _____

_____

Keywords: _____

_____

Images of note: _____

_____

First Reaction to Sign, Event or Card

My Intuitive Response

Angel Guidance

Notes

Angel Journal

Date: _____ Situation: _____

Question _____

_____

Card or Sign: _____

_____

Keywords: _____

_____

Images of note: _____

_____

First Reaction to Sign, Event or Card

My Intuitive Response

Angel Guidance

Notes

Angel Journal

Date: _____ Situation: _____

Question _____

_____

Card or Sign: _____

_____

Keywords: _____

_____

Images of note: _____

_____

First Reaction to Sign, Event or Card

My Intuitive Response

Angel Guidance

Notes

Angel Journal

_____

_____

_____

_____

_____

_____

_____

_____

_____

_____

_____

_____

_____

_____

_____

_____

Date: _____ Situation: _____

Question _____

_____

Card or Sign: _____

_____

Keywords: _____

_____

Images of note: _____

_____

First Reaction to Sign, Event or Card

My Intuitive Response

Angel Guidance

Notes

Angel Journal

_____

_____

_____

_____

_____

_____

_____

_____

_____

_____

_____

_____

_____

_____

_____

_____

Date: _____ Situation: _____

Question _____

_____

Card or Sign: _____

_____

Keywords: _____

_____

Images of note: _____

_____

First Reaction to Sign, Event or Card

My Intuitive Response

Angel Guidance

Notes

Angel Journal

_____

_____

_____

_____

_____

_____

_____

_____

_____

_____

_____

_____

_____

_____

_____

_____

Date: _____ Situation: _____

Question _____

_____

Card or Sign: _____

_____

Keywords: _____

_____

Images of note: _____

_____

| First Reaction to Sign, Event or Card |

| My Intuitive Response |

| Angel Guidance |

| Notes |

Angel Journal

Date: _____ Situation: _____

Question _____

_____

Card or Sign: _____

_____

Keywords: _____

_____

Images of note: _____

_____

First Reaction to Sign, Event or Card

My Intuitive Response

Angel Guidance

Notes

Angel Journal

Date: _____ Situation: _____

Question _____

_____

Card or Sign: _____

_____

Keywords: _____

_____

Images of note: _____

_____

First Reaction to Sign, Event or Card

My Intuitive Response

Angel Guidance

Notes

Angel Journal

_____

_____

_____

_____

_____

_____

_____

_____

_____

_____

_____

_____

_____

_____

_____

Date: _____ Situation: _____

Question _____

_____

Card or Sign: _____

_____

Keywords: _____

_____

Images of note: _____

_____

┌─────── First Reaction to Sign, Event or Card ───────┐

└───┘

┌──────────────── My Intuitive Response ─────────────┐

└───┘

┌──────────────────── Angel Guidance ────────────────┐

└───┘

┌─────────────────────── Notes ──────────────────────┐

└───┘

Angel Journal

Date: _____ Situation: _____

Question _____

_____

Card or Sign: _____

_____

Keywords: _____

_____

Images of note: _____

_____

First Reaction to Sign, Event or Card

My Intuitive Response

Angel Guidance

Notes

Angel Journal

Date: _____ Situation: _____

Question _____

_____

Card or Sign: _____

_____

Keywords: _____

_____

Images of note: _____

_____

First Reaction to Sign, Event or Card

My Intuitive Response

Angel Guidance

Notes

Angel Journal

Date: _____ Situation: _____

Question _____

_____

Card or Sign: _____

_____

Keywords: _____

_____

Images of note: _____

_____

First Reaction to Sign, Event or Card

My Intuitive Response

Angel Guidance

Notes

Angel Journal

Made in the USA
Lexington, KY
25 August 2019